RICHARD CHISHOLM

Meet Me in Istanbul

INTERMEDIATE LEVEL

Founding Editor: John Milne

The Macmillan Readers provide a choice of enjoyable reading materials for learners of English. The series is published at six levels – Starter, Beginner, Elementary, Pre-intermediate, Intermediate and Upper.

Level control
Information, structure and vocabulary are controlled to suit the students' ability at each level.

The number of words at each level:

Starter	about 300 basic words
Beginner	about 600 basic words
Elementary	about 1100 basic words
Pre-intermediate	about 1400 basic words
Intermediate	about 1600 basic words
Upper	about 2200 basic words

Vocabulary
Some difficult words and phrases in this book are important for understanding the story. Some of these words are explained in the story and some are shown in the pictures. From Pre-intermediate level upwards, words are marked with a number like this: ...³. These words are explained in the Glossary at the end of the book.

Contents

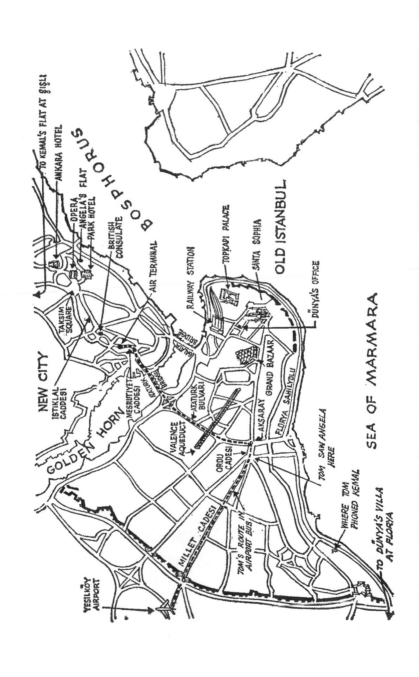

1

Journey to Istanbul

It is early morning on a sunny spring day in April. Heathrow Airport, London, is busy, as usual. Hundreds of people are arriving, leaving, or waiting for planes.

In the Departure Lounge of Terminal One, a man is sitting reading a newspaper. He does not like airports. There are too many people, and he is always nervous[1] when he flies. He looks at his watch impatiently[2]. Then he hears the announcement over the loudspeakers.

'British Airways announce the departure of Flight BE570 for Istanbul. Will passengers please proceed to Gate 16 for boarding[3].'

Tom Smith picks up his suitcase and walks towards Gate 16.

Twenty minutes later, the plane is preparing to leave. It moves slowly across the airport to runway number two. Tom is sitting looking out of the window.

The plane suddenly moves forward, races down the runway and rises into the air. Tom looks down at the houses and roads far below, and smiles. London is behind him. Now he is on his way to Istanbul.

Tom relaxed[4] and took a letter from his pocket.

> *Resat Bey Apt 11-3,*
> *Kamerot Sokak,*
> *Ayazpasa, Istanbul*

My dear Tom,

Thank you for your letter. I am so happy that you can come and visit me for a holiday. Life here in Istanbul is very interesting. I am enjoying my work, but I miss you very much. It will be wonderful to see you again.

I'm sure we will have a very nice holiday. Spring is here, and the weather is beautiful.

I have to work on Monday 14th of April – the day you arrive. So I can't come to the airport to meet you, but you can take a taxi from the Air Terminal to Taksim Square. That's in the centre of the new part of the city. There's a big hotel called the Park Hotel near the square. I'll meet you there at 5 o'clock. We'll meet in the American Bar. The view over the city is beautiful.

I can't wait to see you again, Tom. I have so much to tell you. So remember, the Park Hotel, Taksim Square, 5 o'clock.

See you on the 14th.

love,

Angela.

Tom sat for a moment, looking at his fiancée's[5] letter. Then he put it in his pocket. He looked down at the green fields of France, as the plane continued its journey across Europe.

'Have you been to Istanbul before?' said a voice. It was the young man in the next seat.

'No, I haven't,' said Tom. 'Have you?'

The man smiled.

'My home is in Istanbul. I'm studying in London at the moment. I'm going home for a holiday.'

'Really?' said Tom. 'Where are you studying?'

'At London University.'

The two men sat talking, as the stewardesses[6] began serving lunch. The young man told Tom his name was Kemal. His parents had a shop in Istanbul.

'Are you meeting someone in Istanbul?' Kemal asked.

'My fiancée,' said Tom. 'She's working in Istanbul.'

'That's interesting. How long has she been there?'

She went to Istanbul two months ago. She works for a small

company which is starting to export[7] to England. She's making all the arrangements.'

'Exporting always seems so difficult,' said Kemal.

'It seems difficult,' Tom agreed. 'But that's Angela's job. She's an expert[8] in importing and exporting. Her father has an import/export agency[9] in London and she has worked for him for some years. She's almost completed her work in Istanbul now. The company has already started to send goods to England. She'll be coming back to London soon.'

'What kind of goods do they export?' asked Kemal.

'All kind of things — brass ornaments, coffee-pots, trays leather and onyx articles[10] – Angela's father thinks these goods will sell very well in England.'

'That's interesting,' said Kemal. 'My parents sell things like that in their shop in Istanbul.'

The two men went on talking as the plane flew over Italy and Greece towards Turkey. Soon they were descending to Yesilkoy Airport, Istanbul.

When the plane stopped, Kemal stood up.

'I hope you enjoy your stay in Istanbul,' he said. 'Here's my telephone number. If you need anything, phone me. I live in Sisli. It's not far from the centre of the city.'

'Thanks, Kemal, that's very kind of you.'

'Not at all,' replied Kemal. 'Nice to meet you. And now, goodbye.'

Tom went through Customs and Immigration[11] and walked towards the airport exit.

2

The American Bar

A bus for the City Air Terminal[12] was waiting outside the airport. Tom got in and sat down beside the window. Other passengers got on and the bus left the airport and drove towards Istanbul.

Soon they were driving past the houses and apartment blocks[13] near the city. Then they passed the old city walls. Tom felt excited, and looked at everything. He saw beautiful old mosques[14] and street markets.

The bus was now approaching the centre of old Istanbul. It stopped at some traffic lights.

A car stopped beside the bus. The door opened and a woman got out. Two men were with her. Suddenly Tom jumped to his feet. It was Angela!

'Angela!' Tom shouted. 'Angela! Here! It's me, Tom!'

He knocked on the bus window. Suddenly the traffic lights changed and the bus moved forward. Tom ran to the back of the bus. Angela and the two men were going into a building.

'Angela!' he shouted. 'An . . . ' He stopped. It was too late. The bus was moving quickly down a wide street. The passengers were looking at Tom and he suddenly felt foolish. He walked back to his seat and sat down.

What a surprise, he thought to himself. I must tell her when I see her this evening.

Suddenly Tom jumped to his feet. It was Angela!

Then the bus crossed Ataturk Bridge and Tom looked at the boats on the Golden Horn. Again he felt excited.

The bus arrived at the Air Terminal at a quarter to four. There were some taxis waiting there. Tom went up to one.

'The Park Hotel, Taksim Square, please,' he told the driver.

'English? You come with me. I take you quickly.'

At a quarter past four, the taxi arrived in the square.

'Here you are, sir, the Park Hotel.'

'Thank you,' said Tom, and paid the driver.

Tom went into the hotel. He found the American Bar and sat down at a table on the terrace[15]. A waiter came out.

'A beer, please,' said Tom.

He sat in the afternoon sunshine, and looked down over the city of Istanbul. The view was very beautiful. He was looking at the sea. The Bosphorus was full of ships. There were very big ships going to Russia and little sailing ships. In the distance, he could see the mosques and palaces[16] of old Istanbul. How beautiful and how exciting!

Tom looked at his watch. It was nearly five o'clock. He got up and walked up to the hotel entrance. There were lots of people going in and out of the hotel. But he did not see Angela anywhere. He went back to the bar and ordered another beer.

Come on Angela, Tom said to himself. Don't be late.

Just inside the American Bar a man in a grey raincoat was sitting at a table. He was drinking coffee and smoking cheap cigarettes. A newspaper lay open on the table in front of him, and from time to time he looked at it. But the man wasn't reading the newspaper – he was watching Tom.

It was now twenty past five. Tom sat in the evening sunshine. He looked at his watch again, and waited. Half past five. Quarter to six. It was getting dark. He looked at the lights on the Bosphorus. Strange, thought Tom. Angela isn't usually late.

Tom sat at the table, on the terrace of the American Bar, waiting for his fiancée. He waited, and waited, and nobody came.

And the man in the grey raincoat sat patiently inside the bar, smoking, and watching Tom.

———

'Another beer, sir?' asked the waiter.

'No, bring me a black coffee, please. Have you a telephone?'

'Yes, sir, inside.'

Tom went into the hotel. There was a telephone beside the reception[17]. Tom dialled Angela's number. The phone rang and rang, but nobody answered it. He put the phone down and turned towards the reception desk.

'Excuse me,' he asked the receptionist, 'Kamerot Sokak – do you know where it is?'

'Yes, it's very near. Go out of the hotel entrance and turn right. Walk along the street – and Kamerot Sokak is fourth on the right.'

'Thank you,' said Tom.

Tom went back to the bar. He drank his coffee and paid for his drinks. It was now after eight o'clock. Tom picked up his suitcase and left the hotel.

Inside the bar, the man in the grey raincoat stood up and picked up his newspaper. He put some money on the table and walked out into the street. He stood on the pavement for a moment or two, then started walking.

3

A Shock

Kamerot Sokak was a narrow, quiet street of old apartment buildings. Tom walked along the pavement, looking at the numbers on the doors. There was only one street light and it was difficult to see. But finally, he found Angela's address, number 11.

The building had a large glass door. Tom pushed it, but it was locked. There was no bell. He knocked on the door. Nothing happened. He knocked again, louder this time, and listened. Silence.

Damn[18], he thought. He was impatient now. And worried.

He stood back in the middle of the street and looked up. There were five floors, and all the windows were black. There was no light anywhere in the building.

Angela, he said to himself, Angela! Where are you?

A short distance away, the man in the grey raincoat stood in a dark doorway. He was watching Tom, watching every move he made . . .

Tom did not know what to do. He knocked once more on the glass door – again nothing happened. Finally, he picked up his suitcase. With a last look at the building, he turned and started walking back towards Taksim Square.

Tom Smith, he thought to himself, as he walked. You need a hot bath and a good sleep. Then you can decide what to do.

The Park Hotel was expensive, but Tom remembered seeing

one or two small hotels near Taksim Square. Finally, he was standing outside the Ankara Hotel. He went in.

'Good evening,' he said to the woman at reception. 'I'd like a single room, please.'

The woman nodded.

'We have a nice room upstairs. Come, I'll show you.'

They went upstairs and she opened a door.

'Very nice room,' she said.

It was small, but it was clean and it looked comfortable.

'I'll take it,' he said, and gave the woman his passport.

'The bathroom is along the corridor,' she said. 'Breakfast is from eight to ten o'clock. Goodnight.'

Tom put his case down and sat on the bed. He suddenly felt very tired and unhappy. He was not having a good dinner in a nice restaurant. He was not sitting with the woman he loved. He was sitting alone, in a cheap hotel, in a strange city.

For a long time he sat on the bed thinking, But I *saw* Angela. I saw her from the bus!

Finally he stood up.

OK, he thought. Tomorrow morning I'll go to Angela's office and find out what has happened. There's a very simple explanation, I'm sure. I'll find out tomorrow.

He had a hot bath and got into bed. He was very tired after his long journey and soon fell asleep.

———

The man in the grey raincoat walked across Taksim Square. There was a telephone kiosk[19] in the corner. He dialled a number, and waited. Then he spoke.

'He's in the Ankara Hotel,' the man said. 'He waited at the Park Hotel and then he went to the girl's flat. Now he's in the Ankara Hotel . . . Yes, yes of course I will.'

He put down the phone and left the kiosk.

The next morning, Tom felt much better. He had breakfast, then took a taxi to the office where Angela worked.

The taxi drove through the busy streets and crossed the Galata Bridge into the old city. Finally, it turned into a small street near the Railway Station. It was a narrow street of shops, small businesses and workshops. The taxi stopped in front of a grey building.

"F. Karamian and Co. Export/Import Agency", said the sign above the door. Tom pushed open the door and went in. A secretary was typing at the reception desk. She looked up as Tom came in.

'Good morning,' she smiled.

'Good morning,' said Tom. 'My name's Tom Smith. I'm looking for Angela Thomson – she's my fiancée. I arrived in Istanbul last night and waited for her, but she didn't . . .'

The secretary was staring at him. She stood up.

'Wait a moment, please, Mr Smith.'

She hurried over to a door marked "Office", and went inside. Tom could hear her talking to someone.

The door opened and a man came out. He looked very serious[20].

'Mr Smith, my name's Dünya. Please come in.'

Tom went into the office.

'Please sit down, Mr Smith,' said Dünya. 'Look – er, I don't know how to tell you this, Mr Smith. I have some very bad news for you. I'm very sorry indeed, but Miss Thomson, your fiancée – is – is dead.'

4

'I Saw Her'

'Drink this, Mr Smith,' said Mr Dünya. He handed Tom a glass of strong brandy. Tom sat, shocked, white-faced, unable to speak. He drank the brandy slowly.

'How – how did it happen?' he asked.

'A car accident. Miss Thomson was driving along a dangerous road. No one knows what happened. Her car went off the road and fell down the hillside.'

'Yesterday evening?' Tom asked.

'I beg your pardon[21]?'

'The accident – it happened yesterday evening?'

Dünya looked at him.

'Mr Smith, the accident happened a week ago – last Sunday to be exact. She had been away to Bursa for the weekend and . . .'

'But that's impossible!' said Tom. 'I saw Angela yesterday!'

'Yesterday?'

'Yes. I was on the airport bus, coming into Istanbul. I saw her in the street.'

'I'm terribly sorry, Mr Smith, but you're making a mistake.'

'No, I tell you I saw her. I . . .'

'Mr Smith,' Dünya said patiently, 'Istanbul is a big city. There must be hundreds of women here who look like your fiancée.'

Tom said nothing.

'The British Consulate were very helpful,' continued Mr Dünya. 'They made all the arrangements for the funeral[22]. It was on Wednesday.'

'Have her parents been told about this?' Tom asked.

'That is a problem, I'm afraid. Her parents are on holiday in France. The British and French police are trying to contact[23] them.'

'So they don't know yet,' said Tom quietly.

'No, they don't, I'm afraid.'

There was a long silence.

'Can I have another brandy, please?' asked Tom.

'Of course.'

Tom tried hard to think clearly.

'I thought I saw her yesterday,' he said softly.

'I understand, Mr Smith. It's a great shock – a terrible tragedy[24] for you – for all of us.'

After a pause, Dünya asked, 'What will you do now, Mr Smith? Is there anything I can do to help?'

'I'm not sure,' said Tom. 'I need some time to think. I don't know what to do.'

'Do you know anyone in Istanbul?'

Suddenly Tom remembered Kemal.

'Yes, yes, I have friends, don't worry. Look, Mr Dünya, I can't decide anything now. I think I'll stay in Istanbul for a day or two. I'd like to visit the Consulate, and maybe the police.'

Mr Dünya opened a drawer in his desk and took out a card. He wrote on it and handed the card to Tom.

'I've written down the telephone number of Mr David Pennington. He's the man in the Consulate who made the arrrangements for the funeral. The other number is my office telephone number. Contact me if you need anything. I'm here during the day.'

Tom stood up.

'I must go now,' he said. 'Thank you, you've been most kind.'

Mr Dünya walked with him to the door. 'Well, Mr Smith, once again, I'm terribly sorry.'

'You know I was so sure I saw her. So sure . . .' Tom said.

'I understand,' replied Dünya. 'It's a terrible shock.'

The two men shook hands.

'Remember, come here any time if you need anything,' said Mr Dünya. 'Goodbye, now.'

'Goodbye,' said Tom, and walked out into the street.

Mr Dünya turned and walked back into his office. He closed the door carefully and sat down at his desk. For a few minutes he sat thinking. Then he picked up the telephone.

Tom walked slowly through the crowded streets of old Istanbul. The streets were busy, and full of interesting people, shops and cafés. But Tom did not see any of those things. He was not interested in Istanbul, he was not a tourist any more. Tom was thinking of Angela. He remembered the journey on the bus from the airport. He was sure he had seen Angela. She had been there on the pavement, getting out of a car. But Dünya said it was not Angela. Angela was dead. She had died a week ago.

Tom walked through the streets of the city. He walked through the Grand Bazaar. He walked on and on through narrow old streets. He didn't know where he was, or what time it was. He thought about Angela. He thought again about his journey on the bus from the airport. Again and again he thought about it, and again and again he saw his fiancée. Then he stopped walking, and stood for a moment on the pavement. He was standing on a street beside the sea.

18

Angela isn't dead, he thought. I saw her!

He looked in his pocket and found Kemal's telephone number. He walked quickly across the street to a café. He went inside to the telephone.

'Hello, Kemal? Hello, it's me, Tom. Remember . . .? Yes, yes, fine thanks. Listen, remember you said I could phone you if I needed anything? Well, something has happened. Can we meet somewhere?'

5

A Disappointing Day

'So,' said Kemal, 'you really think you saw her, do you?' Kemal and Tom were sitting in the American Bar at the Park Hotel. Tom thought carefully for a moment before answering.

'Yes,' he said slowly. 'Yes, I do. You probably think I imagined[25] it. I understand that. But I'm convinced[26] I saw her, that's all.'

19

Kemal nodded.

'I can't stop thinking about yesterday,' Tom continued. 'I close my eyes and I can see Angela there on the pavement. I can't forget that.'

'Listen, Tom,' said Kemal. 'We only met yesterday but already we're friends. You're in my country, you're my friend, and you need help. If you think you saw Angela, that's enough for me. I believe you. Now we have to decide what to do.'

'There are two things I want to do as soon as possible,' said Tom. 'I want to go to the street where I saw Angela. Then I want to go to the British Consulate. I have an appointment[27] for this afternoon.'

'OK,' said Kemal. 'The street where you saw Angela. Do you think you can remember where it is?'

'No problem,' said Tom. 'We can drive along the same route as the airport bus. I'm sure I'll remember it.'

'And what do you think you will find there?'

'I'm not sure. But she was going into a building with two men. At least we can find the building – maybe that will tell us something.'

'OK,' said Kemal. 'My car's outside. Let's go.'

———

Tom and Kemal were driving through the city.

'It was a wide street,' said Tom. 'We came to a roundabout[28] after the traffic lights. We turned left and then we passed an old aqueduct[29].' أكردات

'Aksaray,' said Kemal. 'It's near here.'

Kemal drove over Ataturk Bridge. After a few minutes, they saw the old aqueduct. Then they came to a large roundabout and turned right.

'This is it,' said Tom. 'It's somewhere near here.'

They were approaching some traffic lights. Tom looked out of the window at the buildings on the left.

'No,' he said. 'Not here.'

They drove on to the next traffic lights.

'This is it,' said Tom. 'This is the place.'

Kemal stopped the car.

'You get out. I'll find a parking place.'

Tom got out and looked around him. He was in a wide street of shops and offices. A newspaper kiosk, a travel agency – he remembered them from the day before. He stood looking at the buildings opposite until Kemal arrived.

Tom pointed across the street to the entrance to an office building.

'That's it, I think,' he said.

They crossed the street and looked at the name plate beside the entrance to the office block. There were many names there a lawyer, a dentist, a doctor, and many other offices. Tom stood looking at the names for a few moments.

'Well,' he said finally, 'I'm sure she went into this building. But which office was she going to? Was she going to see a lawyer, or a dentist, or a doctor? How do we begin to find out?'

Kemal took his arm gently, and they walked slowly back to the car.

'Listen, Tom,' he said. 'You're going too fast. You can't expect to find out everything immediately. Wait until you see the man at the Consulate. After that, we'll think about it. Then we can decide what to do. We know she was going into that building. That's something, anyway. Now look, it's lunch-time. You must be hungry. I know a good restaurant near here . . .'

'You're right,' said Tom. 'We have to be patient.'

6

Visit to the Consulate

After lunch, Kemal drove Tom to the British Consulate in Mesrutiyet Street. He stopped the car at the gate.

'Well, good luck,' he said. 'I'll wait for you.'

Tom opened the car door.

'It's very good of you to help me like this Kemal. Thanks very much.'

'Not at all,' said Kemal. 'See you later.'

Tom went through the Consulate gates. The old Consulate, with beautiful gardens round it, looked like a palace. Tom pushed the big door open and went in.

'I'd like to see Mr David Pennington, please,' he said at the reception desk. 'My name's Tom Smith. I have an appointment.'

After a few minutes, a tall man wearing glasses came to meet him.

'Mr Smith, my name's Pennington. How do you do?' said the man, holding out his hand.

Tom shook Mr Pennington's hand. 'How do you do,' he replied.

'Come into my office, please, Mr Smith. Mr Dünya told me you were coming.'

They walked up the beautiful staircase of the Consulate and went into Mr Pennington's office.

'Sit down, please,' said Pennington. 'Mr Smith, I'm very sorry about your fiancée. It was a great tragedy. Please accept my condolences[30].'

'Thank you,' said Tom.

Mr Pennington took two files[31] from his desk.

'This is our report on the accident,' he said. 'And this is the police report. I can give you copies of these, but perhaps you'd like to ask me some questions first.'

Tom thought for a moment.

'Mr Pennington,' he said, 'I think I saw Angela yesterday.'

Pennington stared[32] at Tom. There was silence in the room. Pennington looked down at his desk, then he looked at Tom again. Tom was able to hear the noise of the traffic in the street outside the gardens. For a long time Pennington said nothing. At last he spoke.

'Mr Smith,' he said, 'I don't think you fully understand. Your fiancée . . .'

'I know,' Tom interrupted. 'Angela was killed in a road accident last weekend. Her funeral was last Wednesday. Mr Dünya told me that this morning. But I'm telling you I saw her yesterday.'

'Mr Smith, I think you should read these reports carefully before you say anything more.'

He passed the files over to Tom.

'Can I get you a cup of tea or something?'

'A cup of tea would be nice. Thank you.'

Pennington left the office. He came back a few minutes later with some tea. There was silence in the room while Tom read the reports. Presently he looked up.

'After the accident,' Tom asked Pennington, 'how did they identify[33] the body?'

'That was difficult,' said Pennington. 'As you know, the accident happened on a dangerous road about 200 kilometres from here. Your fiancée's car crashed through a wall by the side of the road, and fell down the hillside. The car burst into flames[34] and was completely burned out. The – the body was very badly burned, so identification was difficult. But the police found your fiancée's handbag lying near the car. Her passport and papers were in the handbag. The police found out that the car was owned by a car hire company[35]. Miss Thomson had hired the car for the weekend.'

'What about Angela's parents?' Tom asked.

'I'm afraid her parents don't know about the accident yet. They're on a camping holiday in France – the police are trying to contact them.'

'What was she doing on that dangerous road?'

'She spent the weekend in Bursa, sightseeing[36]. It's a very interesting old town. She was on her way back to Istanbul.'

Tom thought for a moment.

'And are the police quite satisfied[37]?' Tom asked.

'Yes,' said Pennington. 'The police are convinced that it was an accident. The file is closed[38].'

'And you people at the Consulate,' said Tom quietly, 'are you satisfied?'

For a moment Pennington said nothing.

'Yes, Mr Smith, we are,' he said. 'Our job, among other things, is to look after British citizens in Turkey. We have looked into this matter very carefully. And we are satisfied that it was an accident.'

Tom said nothing.

'I really am very sorry,' Pennington went on. 'I understand how you must feel. You've had a terrible shock. My advice to you now is to leave Istanbul. There is nothing you can do here.'

'I'm beginning to think you're right,' said Tom. 'Perhaps I should go home. You know, I really thought I saw Angela, but now . . .'

'Where are you staying?' asked Pennington.

'The Ankara Hotel, near Taksim Square.'

'Will you be all right? Do you know anyone here?'

'I'm all right, thank you. I have a friend here.'

'Well Mr Smith, please think carefully about what I've said. I hope you'll take my advice. If you need anything before you leave, contact me. I'll be glad to help you.'

'Thank you,' said Tom, standing up. 'Thank you for all you've done.'

'Not at all,' said Pennington. 'I'm sorry your visit to Istanbul wasn't a happier one. Have a good journey home. Goodbye.'

The two men shook hands and Tom left the Consulate.

7

The Man in the Grey Raincoat

Kemal was waiting in the car outside the Consulate gates. 'What did he say?' Kemal asked, as Tom got in the car.

'The same as Dünya,' Tom replied. 'It was an accident. Angela's dead. The file is closed.'

Kemal started the car, and drove away from the Consulate.

'Mr Pennington advised me to go back to London,' Tom continued. 'I'm beginning to think he's right.'

Kemal said nothing.

'The police think Angela is dead, and the people at the Consulate do too. I'm the only person who doesn't think she's dead. So what am I going to do? Stay here in Istanbul? Go home? Really, I just don't . . .'

'Now wait a minute, wait a minute, Tom,' said Kemal. 'How long have you been in Istanbul?'

'Not very long . . .'

'You've been here less than twenty-four hours. And what has happened to you in this time? You've had a terrible shock. You've been told that your fiancée was killed in an accident a week ago. But you are sure you saw her from the bus last night. So now you are confused and you don't know what to do. That's right, isn't it?'

Tom nodded his head slowly in agreement.

'Well, I'll tell you what you're going to do,' Kemal went on. 'You're going to come with me to the Topkapi Palace. We can walk through the beautiful gardens there and think about everything carefully. Then we can decide what to do next.'

Tom smiled.

'You're right, of course. It has been a difficult day.'

'Exactly,' said Kemal. 'Now it's time to relax a little.'

They were driving down narrow streets, to the Golden Horn.

'This is the Galata Bridge – it crosses the Golden Horn,' said Kemal. 'Look, isn't it beautiful?'

They drove slowly across the bridge in the bright sunlight.

'It is beautiful,' said Tom, looking out across the Bosphorus. 'Very beautiful.'

They continued across the bridge, turned left, and drove past the Railway Station. A few minutes later they came to Santa Sophia – one of the oldest and most beautiful buildings in Istanbul. It was once a church, then a mosque and now it is a museum[39].

'We'll leave the car here,' said Kemal. 'First, I'm going to show you the Palace of Topkapi.'

They got out of the car in a large park. They were standing in front of the first gate of the Palace.

'The Sultans[40] of Turkey used to live in Topkapi Palace,' Kemal explained.

Kemal and Tom bought an entrance ticket. They walked through the gate into the gardens of the Palace.

'This is the first courtyard of the Palace,' went on Kemal. 'Over there are the royal kitchens. And over there the harem – that's part of the Palace where the women lived.'

They were walking down a wide path. Kemal looked round and then he took Tom by the arm.

'Walk a little faster,' he said quietly.

Tom saw that there was a strange look on Kemal's face.

'Is anything wrong?' he asked.

'Keep walking,' said Kemal. 'And don't look back.'

They walked across the courtyard towards the second gate of the Palace.

'Kemal, what's wrong?' said Tom quickly.

'Someone is following us,' answered Kemal.

'Someone following us?' said Tom. 'What do you mean?'

'There's a man in a grey raincoat walking behind us. I saw

Kemal and Tom walked through the gate into the gardens of the Palace.

him when we came into the Palace. I wasn't sure at first, but I am sure now.'

They walked on and then ran through the second gateway. Kemal looked back. The man was still following them.

'This way. Quickly.' Kemal led Tom to the entrance of the Treasury[41]. Inside, it was very crowded and it was also dark after the bright sunshine.

'We're going to separate[42] now,' said Kemal. 'The man won't be able to follow both of us. You take a taxi back to your hotel. Have you got some money?'

'Yes,' said Tom.

'Right, I'll phone you this evening.'

'What are you going to do?' asked Tom.

'I'm going back to my car.'

'Be careful,' said Tom.

'You too,' said Kemal. 'See you later.'

8

A Surprise Phone Call

It was seven o'clock when Tom arrived in Taksim Square. He got out of the taxi and walked towards his hotel. He felt nervous. Was someone watching him? Was someone sitting in a car watching his hotel? He hurried inside.

'Good evening,' said the woman at reception.

'Good evening,' said Tom.

He took his room key and went upstairs. He locked his door, took off his shoes and lay down on the bed. He felt tired, but nervous and excited at the same time. For a long time he lay on the bed, listening to the noises in the street outside, and thinking about one person – Angela.

The phone rang. It rang loudly, and Tom jumped nervously.
Kemal, he thought, and picked up the receiver.
'Yes?'
'This is reception, Mr Smith, I have a call for you.'
'Thank you,' said Tom.
'Hello? Is that Tom Smith?' It was a woman's voice.
'Yes. Who is that?' Tom asked. His heart was beating fast.
'You don't know me, Mr Smith, but I'm a friend of Angela's.
I have something to tell you. Can we meet somewhere?'
'Who are you?'
'My name's Julie. As I said, I'm a friend of Angela's. Listen, I
don't want to talk on the phone. Can we meet somewhere?'
'Yes, yes, sure,' said Tom, thinking quickly. 'Do you know the
American Bar at the Park Hotel?'
'I know it. I'll be there in twenty minutes.'
There was a click and then there was silence.
Tom put the phone down and jumped to his feet.
'I must tell Kemal,' he said to himself.
He picked up the phone.
'Reception? Can I have Istanbul 36 82 45?'
Tom waited impatiently.
'Sorry, sir, there's no answer,' said the woman at reception.
'OK, I'll try later.'
Tom put the phone down, and left the room.

———

There were only a few people in the American Bar when Tom
went in. He sat down at a table by a window. From there he could
see everyone who came through the door.

Tom sat drinking a beer and watching the door. Who was
Julie? What did she want? Tom would soon find out.

A girl came in a few minutes later. She had long blonde hair, and was wearing jeans. The girl looked round the bar, then walked over to Tom's table.

'Hi,' she said. 'I'm Julie.'

'Hello,' he said. 'I'm Tom. Please sit down.'

She sat down. The waiter came over.

'Would you like a drink?' said Tom.

'A coffee, please,' she said. The waiter nodded and left.

'So you're Tom,' Julie said. 'You look just like your photograph. Angela showed me a picture of you.'

'But how did you find me?' Tom asked.

'I went to the British Consulate today,' Julie explained. 'I spoke to Mr Pennington; he told me the name of your hotel. I knew you were coming to Istanbul and I wanted to speak to you.'

She looked round nervously.

'Listen, Tom,' she went on. 'There's something strange going on. What do you know about Angela's accident?'

'Only what the Consulate told me today,' said Tom. He told Julie about his conversation with Mr Pennington.

'And are you satisfied?' she asked.

Tom looked at her.

'Tell me what you think,' he said slowly.

'All right,' said Julie. 'Let's start at the beginning. Angela

31

came to Istanbul two months ago. I met her at a party soon after she arrived and we became good friends. At the beginning, she was happy. She enjoyed her job, she liked working for her boss . . .'

'Dünya ?'

'That's right. Everything was fine. I saw her quite often. We used to have lunch together, and go sightseeing. And then, two weeks ago something happened. Angela seemed worried about something – something to do with her work. I asked her what was wrong but she didn't want to talk about it. Then one lunch-time we were together in a restaurant and suddenly Dünya came in. The moment she saw him, she became nervous. I think she was afraid of him.'

'Go on,' Tom said.

'Well, I don't know anything else. She never told me what she was worried about. I saw her a few more times, and then she had the accident.'

She looked at Tom.

'But it is strange, isn't it?' Julie went on. 'She was worried about something – her job, or her boss, or something. But she wouldn't talk about it. And then she had an accident.'

She stopped.

'That's all,' she said. 'That's what I wanted to tell you.'

Tom leant across the table.

'Shall I tell you something?' he said quietly. 'Yesterday, on the way into Istanbul, I saw her.'

Julie stared at him.

'Where?' she asked.

'I was in the airport bus, coming into the city. We were in Millet Street near Aksaray. Angela was going into a building with two men.'

'What do you mean, going into a building? Which building?'

'Well, I don't know. There are a lot of offices in the building. I went there today. There was a dentist, and a doctor . . .'

'Doctor,' said Julie. 'That's interesting.'

'What do you mean?'

'Angela had a virus[43] two weeks ago – a bad attack. She was getting pills from a doctor. That explains it – she needed more pills, or treatment. She was going to a doctor!'

Tom thought for a moment.

'So that's where she was going,' he said. 'To the doctor's. Maybe I can go and ask the doctor a few questions.'

Julie looked worried.

'Be careful, Tom,' she said.

'What do you mean?'

'Just be careful,' she repeated. 'Something strange is happening. It could be dangerous for you if you ask too many questions.'

'OK,' said Tom. 'But I'm sure Angela is in this city somewhere. She's in trouble. The police and the Consulate say she's dead, so they won't help. But I think she's alive. She's in Istanbul somewhere, and I'm not leaving until I find her!'

9

'*Goodbye, Mr Dünya*'

Later that evening Tom phoned Kemal. He told him about his meeting with Julie. Kemal listened while Tom explained what had happened.

'OK,' he said, when Tom had finished. 'Listen – I think I understand what's happening. Angela was working for Dünya. Right?'

'Yes.'

'And then she was worried about something – something at work. Right?'

'Yes.'

'OK, and then she had her accident. But it wasn't an accident. Tom – you know what I think? I think Angela is alive. She's here somewhere in Istanbul. Dünya is holding her prisoner[44].'

'What?'

'Think about it, Tom. Angela was worried about something at work. We think it was something to do with Dünya and his export business. And now she has disappeared. But she isn't dead – there was no car accident – Dünya is holding her prisoner, I'm sure of it.'

'But,' began Tom. 'I don't . . .'

'Listen, Tom,' continued Kemal, 'what about the man in the Topkapi Palace today – the man who followed us? You know what I think, Tom? I think Dünya and his friends have been watching you since you arrived in Istanbul. They know where you are staying, they know you went to the Consulate, and that's how they followed us to the Palace today. They know everything about you, Tom.'

'God,' said Tom quietly. 'My God, Kemal, I think you're right. You must be right. But what are we going to do now?'

'I'll tell you,' said Kemal. 'They know where you are staying and they know you're looking for Angela. That's why they're watching you. They want to find out what you do next. Well, I'll tell you what you're going to do next. You're going to leave Istanbul. Now listen . . .'

Next morning, Tom checked out[45] of his hotel.

'Thank you,' he said to the receptionist, 'and goodbye.'

'Leaving Istanbul?'

'Yes, I'm going home.'

'Goodbye, sir. Have a good journey.'

Tom took a taxi to Dünya's office. The driver stopped outside.

'Wait here, please,' said Tom. 'I'll be back in a few minutes.' He went into the office.

'Good morning,' he said to the secretary. 'Is Mr Dünya here? I've come to say goodbye.'

She went to the office. Mr Dünya came out.

'Ah, Mr Smith.'

'Good morning, Mr Dünya. I've come to say goodbye.'

'Leaving so soon?'

'Yes. I went to the British Consulate yesterday and spoke to Mr Pennington. It seems there's nothing I can do here. I'm going back to London. Thank you for your help.'

'You're welcome, Mr Smith. Once again, I'm very sorry about your fiancée. I'm sorry your visit to Istanbul wasn't a happy one.'

'Thank you and goodbye. My plane leaves at midday.'

'At midday? I see. Goodbye, Mr Smith. Have a good journey.'

The two men shook hands. Tom turned and left the office. His taxi was waiting.

'The airport, please,' he said as he got in.

The taxi moved off. Another car, parked twenty metres away, moved away from the pavement and started following.

———

At the airport, Tom walked over to the British Airways desk. He asked about the flight to London, but he did not check in. Then he bought a newspaper and sat down to wait. He looked round the busy airport.

Somewhere among all these people, he thought, someone is watching me.

He opened his newspaper and started reading. Then there was an announcement over the loudspeaker: 'British Airways announce the departure of their flight TK979 for London. Will passengers please proceed to Gate 6 for boarding.'

Tom picked up his things and walked towards passport control. There were lots of people at the entrance to passport control. Tom went into the crowd of people and moved towards a large man whose relatives were saying goodbye. Suddenly he turned and went into the men's toilet. In the toilet he took off his jacket and started to wash his hands and face. No one followed him into the toilet. Then there was another announcement: British Airways Flight TK979 for London. This is the final announcement. Will passengers please proceed immediately to Gate 6. This gate is now closing.'

Tom heard the announcement but didn't move. He looked at his watch, and smiled to himself.

The man in the grey raincoat walked over to the telephone kiosks and dialled a number.

'Hello? I saw him leave. Yes – he's on the plane.'

The man put the phone down and walked away towards the exit.

Half an hour later, Tom was in a taxi on his way to Kemal's flat in Sisli.

Kemal opened the door.

'Hello, Tom,' he smiled. 'Everything OK?'

'No problem,' smiled Tom. 'I went into the crowd at passport control. Then I hid in the toilet at the last minute.'

'Well done. Dünya and his friends will think you have gone back to London. Now you can stay here in my flat and we can start looking for Angela.'

'And we know where to start, don't we?'

'Yes – Dünya's office,' replied Kemal.

Tom went into the crowd of people.

10

An Important Discovery

Kemal and Tom had something to eat. Then they sat down and made their plans for the evening.

'We'll watch Dünya's office this evening,' said Kemal. 'When he comes out we'll follow him. Then we'll find out where he lives.'

'Won't that be dangerous for me?' asked Tom. 'He knows me, remember. What if he sees me?'

Kemal smiled and stood up.

'I've thought about that. And I've got just what you need. Look.'

Kemal opened a drawer.

'Put this on,' he said.

'A wig[46]!' said Tom.

'And a false moustache[47], too. Go on, try them on.'

Tom put on the wig and moustache. He looked in the mirror.

'No one will recognise me now,' he laughed. 'Not even my own mother!'

'Good,' said Kemal. 'And if you also wear dark glasses you will be completely disguised[48].'

It was seven o'clock and the shops and small businesses in the quiet street were closing.

Tom and Kemal sat in the car, waiting patiently.

'He'll be leaving soon,' said Tom.

Further down the street, they could see the entrance to Dünya's office. They sat in silence, watching. Time passed slowly. Ten past seven, quarter past, then suddenly – 'There he is,' whispered Tom. 'That's him.'

Dünya came out of his office and locked the door carefully behind him. He looked along the street. Then walked over to a grey Mercedes car and got in.

The Mercedes moved away from the pavement and drove along the street. It turned right onto the main road.

'Let's go,' said Kemal and drove down the street. They turned right, following the Mercedes. The main road was busy, and they drove along in the traffic.

'There it is,' said Kemal. 'About fifty metres away, in front of that taxi.'

'Careful,' said Tom. 'Don't drive too close. Stay behind the taxi.'

They drove along the main road, watching the Mercedes.

'He's turning left.'

'OK.'

Tom and Kemal followed.

They were now driving along the wide street beside the sea. For twenty minutes they drove towards the suburbs[49] of the city. Now they were outside the city centre and the traffic was moving faster. The Mercedes turned off the main road.

'Slow down,' said Tom. 'You're too near.'

They slowed down until the Mercedes had turned the corner, then drove faster. When they turned the corner, the road was empty.

'Damn,' said Kemal, and drove faster. They crossed another side street, and looked quickly right and left.

'Left,' said Tom. 'There he is!'

They turned and drove along a quiet street of private villas[50]. This was the most dangerous part because there was not much traffic. If Dünya looked round now, he would see that someone was following him . . .

'He's stopping,' said Kemal, as he saw the Mercedes' brake lights going on.

Kemal drove slowly. The Mercedes was now fifty metres in front of them.

'He's turning,' said Kemal.

The Mercedes turned off the street and drove through the gates of a large villa. The villa was surrounded by trees and bushes. Already the gates were closing behind it as the Mercedes drove up to the house.

Tom and Kemal drove past the closed gate and continued along the street.

'Well,' said Tom. 'That's where Dünya lives.'

'That's a start,' said Kemal. 'Come on, let's go home now.'

Back in Kemal's flat, they discussed what they had seen.

'I think that Angela is in the villa,' said Tom.

Kemal agreed.

'What do we do now?' asked Tom. 'We can't get into the villa. There are probably men guarding it.'

'I agree,' said Kemal. 'We think she's in the villa but we can't get in there.'

'It doesn't matter. The villa isn't important,' said Tom.

'What do you mean?'

'Think about it,' Tom replied. 'Remember what Julie said. Angela was worried about something at work. She worked in the office, she never went to the villa. So what we're looking for is in the office. The villa isn't important.'

'You're right,' said Kemal. He stood up and walked over to the window. 'Listen, you've been inside the office, what's it like?'

'When you go in the door,' Tom told him, 'there's the window, and a small reception desk. Then there's an office, and a door to Dünya's private office at the back.'

'Anything else?'

Tom tried to remember the inside of the office.

'Yes,' he said. 'There's a door, another door, at the back.'

'OK,' said Kemal. 'They must have a workshop or a store through that door. That's where they'll keep all the things they export. So somehow we have to have a look inside . . .'

Kemal thought for a moment.

'I've got an idea,' he said suddenly. 'Dünya exports onyx ornaments to England. My parents sell things like that in their shop. So, if I had a box of ornaments and I wanted to sell them very cheaply, who would buy them from me?'

Tom looked at him, then smiled.

'Dünya,' he said.

'Exactly,' smiled Kemal. 'Now, let's think carefully . . .'

41

11

A Clever Trick

Ibrahim Dünya was alone in his private office. He was working at his desk, finishing some paperwork. He always did his paperwork alone before going home.

He looked at his watch. Another ten minutes, then he would be finished.

There was a knock at the door.

Dünya looked up from his papers. He didn't move. There was another knock, louder this time.

He put the papers in his desk and locked it. Then he got up and went out into the office. He could see a man outside, standing in the doorway.

'We're closed,' he said through the glass door. 'Come back tomorrow.'

'I'm sorry,' said the man. 'It's urgent[51], please.'

Dünya was annoyed[52]. He unlocked the door and opened it.

'We're closed. Can't you see?'

'I'm very sorry to bother you,' said Kemal. 'But I was hoping to find someone here. I have a problem. You see, I need some money quickly. I must have it tomorrow morning, early. It's for well, it doesn't matter why I need the money. That's my problem. But I have some onyx ornaments to sell and I heard you would be interested.'

He held out a beautiful onyx ashtray.

'Would you be interested in buying fifty of these?'

Dünya took the ashtray and looked at it carefully. Kemal could see he was interested.

'Very good quality,' said Kemal.

'Fifty, did you say?'

'That's right. They're in the car outside.'

'How much do you want?' Dünya asked.

'15,000 lira for fifty,' said Kemal.

'That's too much,' said Dünya. 'I'll give you 5000.'

'Please – I need the money urgently,' said Kemal.

'Then you will accept 5000,' said Dünya.

Kemal looked disappointed[53].

'All right.' he said. 'You can have them for 6000 lira. They're in a big box in the car. Could you help me carry them? They're very heavy.'

Dünya went with him to the car. Together they carried the box into the office.

'This is really very kind of you,' said Kemal. 'They are heavy.'

They carried the box to the back of the office. Kemal looked quickly at the door.

'Have you got a store somewhere?' he asked. 'I'm sure you don't want the box in your office.'

Dünya thought for a moment. He looked at the large box in his small office and said, 'One moment.'

He took a key from his pocket and unlocked the door. They picked up the box and carried it through into the workshop. It was a long, wide room, with windows on one side. There were a lot of articles in the room – onyx tables, lamps, ornaments, brass and leather articles. On a workbench[54], there were rows of tools and cutting equipment[55].

'This is fine,' said Dünya. 'Put it down here.'

They put down the box.

Dünya took out his wallet[56]. '6000 lira,' he said.

At that moment the telephone in his office rang. Dünya looked annoyed.

'Excuse me one moment,' he said to Kemal.

He went back to his private office.

Kemal looked at his watch and smiled as Dünya disappeared through the door. Quickly he looked round the workshop. There was a door at the other end. He looked out of the windows.

43

Outside there was a small courtyard[57], and at one end of the courtyard, a wall, two metres high.

On the workbench at the end of the workshop, there were several onyx table lamps. Kemal looked quickly at them. They had been cut in half with a cutting instrument. The inside had been removed. Kemal looked closely.

Suddenly Kemal heard Dünya say goodbye. He turned quickly away from the workbench.

'Sorry to keep you waiting,' Dünya said as he came back in.

'Not at all,' said Kemal. 'I can see you're a very busy man.'

Dünya counted out 6000 lira.

'Thank you,' said Kemal. 'I really need this money. Well, I won't take any more of your time.'

Dünya walked with him to the door into the street.

'Thanks again,' said Kemal. 'Goodnight.'

'Goodnight,' said Dünya, and closed the door.

Kemal went back to his car and drove home. Tom was waiting for him.

'Did it work?' he asked, as Kemal came into the apartment.

'Perfectly,' smiled Kemal. 'My brother phoned just at the right moment, when we were in the workshop. Dünya believed my story, too. And he gave me a very low price for the onyx.'

'What did you see in the workshop?'

Kemal looked serious.

'Well, not very much, I'm afraid. It's just a workshop, or a store. There were lots of onyx and leather articles, brass and tools. And there were some onyx lamps being repaired, I think. But there's a courtyard outside, and another building opposite. I'm sure that it belongs to Dünya. And more important – there's a wall at one end of the courtyard, which isn't too high . . .'

'Meaning?'

'Meaning that it wouldn't be too difficult to climb over it . . .'

12

Disaster!

The next morning, after breakfast, Tom and Kemal sat looking at a street map of Istanbul.

'Look here,' Kemal said.

He pointed to a small street.

'Dünya's shop is in this street. Now, look at the street behind his shop. We'll have to find a way into the courtyard from that side.'

'Do you know that part of the city?' asked Tom.

'Not very well. As far as I remember, there are only offices, warehouses[58] and workshops there. At night it will be quiet, but we'll have to be very careful.'

'OK, we'll do it tonight,' said Tom.

———

They left Kemal's flat in Sisli at ten o'clock and drove across the city to Dünya's shop. They parked the car two blocks from the workshop. There were not many street lights there and it was dark.

'Come on,' said Kemal. 'We must walk from here.'

They walked along the dark streets. They were both wearing dark clothes. They came to the street which ran behind Dünya's workshop and courtyard.

'You see?' said Kemal quietly. 'Only offices, warehouses and workshops – nobody lives in this street. The courtyard must be up this alleyway[59], behind these buildings.'

They looked up and down the dark street. No cars, no one in sight.

'Let's go,' whispered Kemal.

They walked quickly up the alleyway. Tom's heart was beating fast, his mouth dry with fear. They stood behind one of the warehouses, beside the courtyard wall. Somewhere in the distance a dog barked.

'Help me up,' whispered Kemal. 'Quietly!'

Tom stood with his back against the wall. He held his hands together. Kemal put his foot in Tom's hands and reached up.

'OK,' Kemal whispered.

Kemal looked carefully over the wall. The courtyard was empty.

Kemal pulled himself up and sat on top of the wall.

'Give me your hand,' whispered Kemal down to Tom. 'I'll pull you up.'

Tom reached up. Kemal took his hand and pulled. Tom put his other hand on the top of the wall and climbed on to the wall beside Kemal.

Kemal dropped silently to the ground in the courtyard. Suddenly there was a noise. It came from inside the workshop.

Kemal pointed to the side. They hurried silently over to the wall, and waited.

Another noise. A door opened and closed inside the workshop. A light came on in the workshop and shone out across the courtyard. Tom and Kemal stood frozen[60] against the wall. They expected a door to open and men to run out into the courtyard. But nothing happened. They heard people talking and moving about inside. Kemal put his mouth close to Tom's ear.

'This is our only chance,' he whispered. 'We have to try to see what they're doing in there.'

They moved very slowly towards the window. It was so quiet that Tom could hear his heart beating. At last they were going to find out what was happening.

There were some men in the workshop. One of them was working with an onyx table lamp. The lamp had been cut in half. He put a small plastic[61] bag inside the lamp. Then he fixed the two halves of the lamp together again.

Tom looked at all the onyx and brass ornaments, the cutting tools, the pile of plastic bags on the table. Suddenly he understood what was happening.

Ornaments for export to England, and inside the ornaments – opium[62]!

'So that's it!' he whispered to Kemal. 'They're smuggling[63] drugs in the ornaments!'

Tom stepped back from the window. Perhaps he was excited by what he had seen. Perhaps he forgot where he was. But suddenly, he put his foot on a stone and slipped.

He put out his hand and knocked against a piece of wood. The piece of wood fell to the ground with a loud crash.

They moved very slowly towards the window. …There were some men in the workshop.

A light came on, a door opened, and men rushed out.

'Run!' shouted Kemal.

'Stop!' shouted a man. 'Catch them!'

Seconds later, Tom and Kemal were at the wall. They jumped, but Tom was too slow. One of the men caught his legs and pulled him to the ground.

Kemal turned to help Tom. Then it was too late. The other men jumped up and pulled him back into the courtyard. A few seconds later it was all over. Tom and Kemal were prisoners.

13

Journey Into Danger

'This way! Hurry up!' said one of the men, pushing Tom and Kemal towards the door of the workshop.

'Get inside!' said the man.

Tom and Kemal stepped inside and stopped, shocked. Dünya was standing in the workshop. He had a gun in his hand. For a few seconds he stared at them silently.

'Well, well,' he said slowly, 'our friend, the Englishman. Very clever. Oh, yes, very clever. And you!'

His face was red with anger as he looked at Kemal. He stepped forward and hit Kemal in the face. Tom moved forward.

'Don't move, or I'll kill you now,' said Dünya. The gun was pointing at Tom. 'Get over there.'

Tom and Kemal stood beside the workbench. Dünya looked at them both for a long moment.

'So,' he said finally. 'You have seen all this.' He pointed to the plastic bags and the onyx ornaments. 'Very clever of you. We should have killed the English girl before. Then this would never have happened.'

'Where is she?' asked Tom. 'Where is Angela?'

'Oh, don't worry about her. She's OK. Let's say – she is a guest at my villa. You'll be able to speak to her very soon – I'm sure you'll have a lot to talk about – before you all die!'

He laughed – a cold, cruel laugh.

'OK, let's go, said Dünya to his men. 'We're taking these two with us.'

The men pushed Tom and Kemal out of the workshop and through the shop to the door. The Mercedes stood in the street.

'Get inside,' said Dünya.

Tom looked up and down the street. But there was no one there to help them.

'Don't try anything foolish, Englishman. You can't escape. Get in.'

Tom and Kemal sat in the back of the car, with a man on each side of them. The others got in the front. They drove away from the shop, turned on to the main road, and drove across the city towards the suburbs.

'Take a look,' said Dünya, smiling. 'Istanbul by night. So many people, so much life. Take your last look at it, you foolish young men. It's the last time you'll see it.'

'What,' began Tom, 'has Angela got to do with this?'

'We needed her at the beginning,' replied Dünya. 'She was very useful. She helped us to arrange the export of the things to England. She didn't know anything about our – our other business. But one day, she left something in the office, and came back for it in the evening. Most unfortunate for her. She saw what we were doing. After that, I could not let her go.'

'Where is she?' asked Tom urgently.

'Ah – I'm not a cruel man,' replied Dünya. 'I did not kill her. I have kept her in my villa.'

'That's because you didn't know what to do,' said Tom.

'Exactly. But we have no choice now. You know too much about us.'

'What about the drugs when they arrive in Europe?' asked Tom.

'That's easy,' replied Dünya. 'We have friends in England. The goods are delivered to dealers[64] in England and our friends buy them. Your fiancée helped us a lot. I shall soon be rich – very rich.'

The Mercedes turned off the main road, and drove along the small street towards Dünya's villa. The car drove in through the gates of the villa, up to the house. It stopped near the front door. It was a big villa with three floors. There were steps leading up to the front door.

'Out,' said Dünya.

They got out of the car. There was one small light above the front door of the villa. The rest of the house was in complete darkness. Tom looked around – he was looking for a way to escape[65]. Dünya saw him.

51

'If you try to escape, I'll shoot you,' he said. 'Now, get inside.'

They started walking up the steps to the front door.

'STOP!' shouted a voice.

Suddenly a blinding light[66] came on. The garden of the villa was full of men running towards them. For a second Dünya stood frozen on the steps, shocked. Then he ran towards the door. It opened suddenly and two men jumped out. They had guns pointing at Dünya.

'Stop! This is the police. Stop or we'll shoot!'

Dünya dropped his gun and slowly put his hands above his head. His men did the same.

'The police,' Kemal said. 'We're safe.'

At that moment the door of the villa opened and a girl ran out.

'Tom!' she shouted. 'Tom!'

Tom turned round quickly.

'Angela!' For a long time they stood, unable to speak, holding each other.

'Oh, Tom,' said Angela. 'You're here at last!'

He looked into her eyes. 'Angela, my love,' he whispered. 'Are you all right?'

'Oh, yes, I'm all right. I'm fine. The police came here to the villa about an hour ago. We knew you were coming, the police were following you. Oh, Tom, I was so worried that Dünya would kill you.'

She put her arms round him again.

'Oh,' said Tom suddenly. 'Angela, my love, I want you to meet a very good friend of mine.' He turned and smiled at Kemal.

'Angela, this is Kemal.'

'Hello, Kemal, nice to meet you,' said Angela.

'Hello,' he said. 'I've never met you before, but I feel I know you very well!'

They laughed.

'Kemal has been wonderful,' said Tom. 'Without his help, we wouldn't be here now.'

'Stop! This is the police. Stop or we'll shoot!'

'Oh, I only helped you a little,' said Kemal.

'A little!' said Tom.

They watched as Dünya and his men were taken to a police car.

'How did the police know what was happening?' asked Tom.

At that moment a car drove up to the villa. A man got out of the car and walked towards them. He smiled.

'Hello, Mr Smith,' he said. 'We meet again.'

'Mr Pennington!' smiled Tom.

14

Time for a Holiday

Later that night, Tom, Kemal and Angela were relaxing. They were sitting in Mr Pennington's flat in the Consulate building. David Pennington was telling them what had happened.

'Julie came to see me here at the Consulate,' he explained. 'She told me about her conversation with Tom. Then I was convinced that Tom's story was true. I contacted the Turkish police again. After that I tried to contact you, Tom, but you had left your hotel. We thought you'd gone back to England.'

'No,' smiled Tom. He looked at Angela. 'I had some urgent business here in Istanbul.'

They all laughed.

'How did they treat you in the villa?' asked Tom.

'They treated me very well,' replied Angela. 'When my virus was very bad, they took me to the doctor. But I was terribly worried on the Monday you were arriving in Istanbul. Dünya knew you were coming because I had told him earlier. And I knew he was going to send someone to follow you. I was terribly worried.'

'They made a big mistake when they took you to the doctor,' said Tom. 'If I had not seen you from the bus . . .'

'Don't,' said Angela, 'don't even think about it.'

'What about the car accident?' said Kemal. 'How did they arrange that? I wonder whose body was in the burnt out car?'

There was silence while they thought about that. 'The police will have to find that out,' said Pennington finally.

'It was a very clever plan of Dünya's,' said Tom. 'Very clever.'

'Yes,' agreed Pennington. 'And drug-smugglers like Dünya can make millions of pounds.'

'Well – it's over now,' said Angela. She turned to Tom. 'Do you remember the letter I wrote to you Tom? I said that life here in Istanbul is very interesting. I was right, wasn't I?'

They all laughed.

'Yes,' said Tom, 'a little bit too interesting for me! After all this, do you know what I want?'

'What?'

'I want a really dull, uninteresting holiday in Istanbul!'

Points for Understanding

1

1 What was Tom's fiancee's name? What was she doing in Istanbul? Where and at what time had they arranged to meet in Istanbul?
2 What kind of thing did Kermal's parents sell in their shop in Istanbul?
3 What did Kemal give Tom before they said goodbye?

2

1 Who did Tom see when the bus stopped at some traffic lights?
2 There was a man sitting in the American Bar wearing a grey raincoat. What was the man doing?
3 Tom paid for his drinks and left the Park Hotel.
    (a) What was Tom going to do?
    (b) What did the man in the grey raincoat do?

3

1 What did Tom decide to do when he found no one at Angela's flat?
2 What did the man in the grey raincoat do after Tom had gone to bed?
3 What was the bad news that Dünya had for Tom?

4

1 Dünya said Angela had died a week ago. Why did Tom say that was impossible?
2 Dünya gave Tom two telephone numbers. Whose numbers were they?
3 Who did Tom finally phone?

5

1 'That's it, I think,' Tom said to Kemal pointing to a block of offices.
    (a) What did Tom mean by 'That's it'?
    (b) What kind of people had offices in the building?

6

1 What had happened to Angela? How had the police identified her body?
2 What advice did Mr Pennington give Tom?

7

1 What did Kemal notice when he and Tom were walking in the gardens of Topkapi Palace?
2 Why did Kemal and Tom not leave the Palace together?

8

1 Why did Julie think that Angela was afraid of Dünya?
2 Why did Julie think there was something strange about the accident?
3 Why did Julie think Angela was going to see a doctor?
4 What advice did Julie give Tom?

9

1 Tom went to the airport. What was he planning to do?
2 What did the man in the grey raincoat do when Flight TK979 left for London?
3 Where were Tom and Kemal going to start looking for Angela?

10

1 Why did Tom disguise himself with a wig and a false moustache?
2 How did Tom and Kemal find out where Dünya lived? What kind of house did he live in?
3 'I've got an idea,' Kemal told Tom. What was Kemal's idea?

11

1 What happened when Kemal and Dünya were in the workshop?
2 What did Kemal notice at one end of the courtyard?

12

1 What were the men in Dünya's workshop putting into the onyx and brass ornaments?
2 What happened when Tom slipped and knocked over the piece of wood?

13

1 Where was Angela?
2 'What has Angela to do with this?' Tom asked Dünya. What was Dünya's reply?
3 Who was waiting for Dünya at his villa?
4 Who got out of a car and said hello to Tom?

14

1 Why had Pennington become convinced that Tom's story was true?
2 Why was Angela very worried on the Monday Tom was arriving in Istanbul?
3 'After all this, do you know what I want?' said Tom. What did Tom want?

Glossary

1 **nervous** – *to be nervous* (page 5)
   a little frightened.
2 **impatiently** (page 5)
   not wanting to sit and wait any longer. Wanting something to happen.
3 **boarding** (page 5)
   getting on an aeroplane.
4 **relaxed** (page 5)
   sat back and made himself comfortable.
5 **fiancée** (page 6)
   the girl a man is going to marry.
6 **stewardess** (page 6)
   a girl who works on an aeroplane. She looks after the passengers and serves food.

7 **export** (page 7)
to send goods out of one country to sell them in another country. To *import* is to bring goods in from another country.

8 **expert** (page 7)
someone who knows a lot about something.

9 **agency** – *import/export agency* (page 7)
a company which arranges to *export* and *import* goods (see Glossary no. 7 above).

10 **brass ornaments . . . leather and onyx articles** (page 7)
brass ornaments – brass is a bright yellow metal. *Ornaments* are objects which are put in a room to make it beautiful. *Leather* is a material made from animal skin and onyx is a beautiful soft green stone.

11 **Customs and Immigration** (page 8)
when you enter a country the *immigration officials* look at your passport. The *customs officials* look in your luggage to see what kind of things you are bringing into the country.

12 **City Air Terminal** (page 8)
the place in a city where air-passengers take a bus to or from the airport.

13 **apartment block** (page 8)
American English for a block of flats. An apartment block is a large building with a number of flats on each floor.

14 **mosque** (page 8)
a building where someone of the Muslim religion goes to pray.

15 **terrace** (page 10)
in the illustration on page 11, Tom is sitting on the terrace. He is looking down from the terrace onto the city below.

16 **palace** (page 10)
a large beautiful building. Kings, queens and presidents live in palaces.

17 **reception** (page 11)
the place in a hotel where you make inquiries and go to collect the key to your hotel room. A *receptionist* works at the reception in a hotel.

18 **Damn!** (page 12)
a word used by someone to show strong feelings of *impatience* (see Glossary no. 2 above) and to show feelings of anger.

19 **kiosk** (page 14)
    a place in the street from where you can make a telephone call.
20 **serious** (page 15)
    the man was quiet and did not smile because he had bad news to
    tell Tom.
21 **pardon** – *I beg your pardon* (page 16)
    an expression used when you do not understand something, or have
    not heard clearly what someone has said to you.
22 **funeral** (page 17)
    when a dead person is put into the ground.
23 **contact** – *try to contact* (page 17)
    trying to send a message to someone.
24 **tragedy** (page 17)
    a very sad happening.
25 **imagine** (page 19)
    to believe something is true when it is not.
26 **convinced** (page 19)
    very sure about something.
27 **appointment** (page 20)
    an arrangement to meet someone.
28 **roundabout** (page 20)
    where a number of roads meet and the traffic has to go round in a
    circle before turning off.
29 **aqueduct** (page 20)
    a bridge built to carry water above the ground.
30 **condolences** – *Please accept my condolences* (page 23)
    words used to show you feel sorry for someone whose friend or
    relative has died.
31 **file** (page 23)
    papers held together in a cover.
32 **stare** (page 23)
    to look at someone for a long time.
33 **identify** (page 24)
    to say who a dead person is and to name them.
34 **burst into flames** (page 24)
    the car suddenly started burning.
35 **car hire company** (page 24)
    Angela did not have a car. She paid a company to use a car for the
    weekend.

36 *sightseeing* (page 24)
   visiting interesting places and beautiful buildings.
37 *be satisfied* (page 25)
   to believe a story is true and to stop asking questions.
38 *closed* – *the file is closed* (page 25)
   a file is closed when the business is finished. No more questions are
   asked about it.
39 *museum* (page 27)
   a building where old, beautiful and valuable things are kept. People
   visit museums to look at these things.
40 *Sultans* – *The Sultans of Turkey* (page 27)
   the old rulers of Turkey. They were rich and powerful.
41 *Treasury* (page 29)
   the room in the Topkapi Palace where the Sultans kept their
   treasures of gold and silver.
42 *separate* (page 29)
   to go in different directions.
43 *a virus* (page 33)
   an illness. A doctor will give pills or medicine to treat a virus.
44 *prisoner* – *holding her prisoner* (page 34)
   Dünya was keeping Angela locked in a room somewhere.
45 *check out* (page 34)
   when you check out of a hotel you give your key to reception (see
   Glossary no. 17 above) and pay the bill.
46 *wig* (page 38)
   false hair worn on the head.
47 *false moustache* (page 38)
   a moustache is hair growing on a man's upper lip. A false moustache
   is stuck on.
48 *disguised* (page 38)
   when Tom put on the *wig* and false *moustache* (see above) he looked
   different. He was disguised.
49 *suburbs* (page 39)
   the parts of a city away from the centre.
50 *villa* (page 39)
   a large house with beautiful gardens round it.
51 *urgent* (page 42)
   something which is very important and has to be done immediately
   is urgent.

52 **annoyed** (page 42)
upset and angry about something.

53 **disappointed** (page 43)
upset and sad about something.

54 **workbench** (page 43)
a strong table on which things are made.

55 **cutting equipment** (page 43)
tools used to cut through stone and metal.

56 **wallet** (page 43)
a small leather case for holding money.

57 **courtyard** (page 44)
a space behind a house which has walls around it.

58 **warehouse** (page 46)
a building where goods are kept.

59 **alleyway** (page 46)
a small narrow street.

60 **frozen** (page 47)
to be frozen usually means like ice. Here, it means that Tom and
Kemal stood completely still.

61 **plastic** (page 47)
a thin, clear material made into bags.

62 **opium** (page 47)
a drug made from the seeds of the poppy.

63 **smuggle** (page 47)
to take goods from one country to another without going through
customs (see Glossary no. 11 above).

64 **dealers** (page 51)
a dealer is someone who buys and sells goods.

65 **escape-- *to look for a way of escape*** (page51)
to try to get away from someone who is *holding you prisoner* (see
Glossary no. 44 above).

66 **light** – *a blinding light* (page 52)
a light that is shining brightly in your eyes so that you are unable
see properly.

Exercises

Multiple Choice 1

Tick the best answer.

1 Why did Tom go to Istanbul?
a ☐ He went on a business trip to buy carpets.
b ☑ He went to meet his fiancée and have a holiday.
c ☐ He went to buy ornaments for his parents' import/export agency.
d ☐ He went to visit Kemal whose parents have a shop.

2 How did Tom know where to meet Angela?
a ☐ She sent him an e-mail.
b ☐ She phoned him.
c ☐ She left a message at his hotel.
d ☐ She wrote him a letter.

3 How did Angela tell Tom to travel from the airport?
a ☐ By taxi.
b ☐ By bus.
c ☐ On foot.
d ☐ By train.

4 What was Kemal doing in London?
a ☐ He lived there with his family.
b ☐ He was on holiday.
c ☐ He was studying at the university.
d ☐ He was on a business trip.

5 How long had Angela been in Istanbul?
a ☐ For two years.
b ☐ For two weeks.
c ☐ For two months.
d ☐ For two days.

6 Why didn't Angela meet Tom at the airport?
a ☐ Because she had to work at the export company office that day.
b ☐ Because she lived a long way from the airport.
c ☐ Because she didn't know the arrival time of his flight.
d ☐ Because she had to drive to Bursa and wouldn't be back until the afternoon.

Background

This story takes place in the year 1975. Which of the following were not available in 1975?

1 ☐ Postal services such as air mail and telegraph.
2 ☐ Personal computers.
3 ☐ E-mail and the Internet.
4 ☐ Colour television.
5 ☐ Mobile phones.
6 ☐ Car hire.
7 ☐ International telephone calls.

Multiple Choice 2

Tick the best answer.

1 How long was Angela planning to stay in Istanbul?
a ☐ For a few more years.
b ☐ She was planning to come back to London the next day.
c ☐ Not for much longer.
d ☐ For the rest of her life.

2 Why did Kemal give Tom his telephone number?
a ☐ Because he wanted to sell some ornaments to Angela.
b ☐ Because Tom had borrowed something from him.
c ☐ Because he wanted to visit him when they got back to England.
d ☐ Because they got on well and he wanted Tom to call him if he had any problems.

3 Where did Tom expect to stay in Istanbul?
a ☐ At the Park Hotel.
b ☐ At the Ankara Hotel.
c ☐ With Kemal's family.
d ☐ At Angela's apartment.

4 Why didn't Tom go straight to Angela's apartment?
a ☐ Because it is easier to find a big hotel than a small apartment in a strange city.
b ☐ Because she didn't want him to see it.
c ☐ Because he didn't know her address.
d ☐ Because he wanted to see the beautiful view over the city from the American Bar.

5 Where did Tom see Angela?
a ☐ She walked past the American Bar.
b ☐ He saw her going into a building from the window of the bus.
c ☐ He saw her at the window of her apartment when he knocked on the door.
d ☐ She was sitting in her office when the bus drove past.

Exchange Rates

The unit of currency in Turkey is the lira. The unit of currency in the UK is the pound.

In this story, Tom brings English pounds to Istanbul and changes them for Turkish lira. He receives 60,000 lira from a money changer at an exchange rate of 200 lira to the pound.
How much English money did Tom change?

£ ....

By the year 2005 the exchange rate had increased almost 10,000 times because of inflation. Roughly how many lira would you have got for one pound at the end of 2004?

L ....

At the American Bar

Complete the gaps. Use each word in the box once.

> front   distance   watching   view   newspaper   looking
> see   bar   ships   late   beer   little   watch   nearly
> walked   hotel   inside   himself   American   raincoat
> exciting   drinking   table   from   cigarettes   people
> open   anywhere   terrace   Russia

Tom sat on the [1]........*terrace*........ of the [2]........................... Bar.
The [3]........................ was very beautiful. He was
[4].. at the sea. The Bosphorus was full of
[5]........................ . There were very big ships going to
[6]........................ and [7]........................ sailing ships. In the
[8]................................, he could [9]........................ the
mosques and palaces of old Istanbul. How beautiful and how
[10]........................!

Tom looked at his [11]........................ . It was [12]........................
five o'clock. He got up and [13]........................ up to the hotel
entrance. There were lots of [14]........................ going in and
out of the [15]........................ . But he did not see Angela
[16]........................ . He went back to the [17]........................
and ordered another [18]........................ .

'Come on Angela,' Tom said to [19]........................ .
'Please don't be [20]........................ .'

Just [21]........................ the American Bar a man in a grey
[22]........................ was sitting at a [23]........................ .
He was [24]........................ coffee and smoking cheap
[25]........................ . A newspaper lay [26]........................
on the table in [27]........................ of him and [28]........................
time to time he looked at it. But the man was not reading the
[29]........................ – he was [30]........................ Tom.

66

What Happened Next?

Number the sentences in the correct order.

☐ First he went to Angela's apartment.

☐ Then he found a room at the Ankara Hotel.

☐ Mr Dünya gave Tom Mr David Pennington's telephone number.

☐ The next day he went to the export office where Angela worked.

☐ He knocked on the door but there was no answer.

☐ He spoke to Mr Dünya, the owner of the export company.

☐ Tom said, 'But that's impossible! I saw Angela yesterday.'

☐ He told Tom that Angela had been killed in an accident a week before.

☐ Mr Dünya said that he had some very bad news.

1 Tom left the American Bar in the Park Hotel at about 8pm.

Making Sentences

Write questions for the answers.

1 *How did Tom meet Kemal?*
....
Tom met Kemal on the plane.

2 *What*
....
Kemal offered to help Tom find out what had happened.

3 *Who*
....
David Pennington was the man at the British Consulate who arranged Angela's funeral.

4 *Who*
....
The police had tried to contact Angela's parents.

5 *How* ....
Angela died when her car hit a wall and fell down the hillside on a dangerous road.

6 *What* ....
The police said that it was an accident.

7 *Why* ....
It was difficult to identify Angela's body because it was so badly burned.

8 *Why* ....

....
They believed the dead person was Angela because the hired car was registered in her name and her passport was found near the crash.

9 *What* ....
Mr Pennington advised Tom to leave Istanbul.

10 *Why* ....
Tom went to the airport to make Mr Dünya and his friends think he had left Istanbul.

Multiple Choice 3

Tick the best answer.

1 What did Julie tell Tom about Angela's death?
a ☐ She said she was going to speak to Mr Pennington at the Consulate.
b ☐ She said Angela had been killed by Mr Dünya.
c ☐ She said she was sure Angela's death was an accident.
d ☐ She said she thought there was something strange going on.

2 What did Julie say about Angela's boss?
a ☐ Angela always got on very well with her boss.
b ☐ Just before her accident, Angela became afraid of Mr Dünya and seemed to have problems at work.
c ☐ Mr Dünya was very cross when he saw Angela in a restaurant with Julie.
d ☐ Angela thought that Mr Dünya was not very good at his job.

3   Where did Tom wait at the airport?
a   ☐ At a bar.
b   ☐ At Gate 6.
c   ☐ In the men's toilet.
d   ☐ At the telephone kiosks.

4   How did Kemal get into Mr Dünya's office?
a   ☐ He sold him some onyx ashtrays.
b   ☐ He pretended to be a delivery man.
c   ☐ He wore a wig and a false moustache.
d   ☐ He asked to buy some ornaments.

5   What did Kemal see inside the workshop?
a   ☐ Leather belts and jackets with false pockets.
b   ☐ Brass trays and tea glasses with special lids.
c   ☐ Leather shoes with hollow heels to hold bombs.
d   ☐ Onyx table lamps with holes in the middle.

6   What did Kemal and Tom think Mr Dünya's business was doing?
a   ☐ Dealing in arms.
b   ☐ Carrying out terrorist acts.
c   ☐ Stealing money.
d   ☐ Smuggling drugs.

7   Dünya caught Tom and Kemal outside the workshop. Where did he take them?
a   ☐ To Angela's apartment.
b   ☐ To his villa.
c   ☐ To the American Bar.
d   ☐ To the police station.

8   What happened at Dünya's villa?
a   ☐ Tom escaped and rescued Angela.
b   ☐ The police were waiting for them and a policeman shouted 'STOP!'
c   ☐ Angela escaped and called the police.
d   ☐ Dünya shot Tom and Kemal.

9 Why had Angela been kept prisoner?
a ☐ Because Dünya wanted to marry her.
b ☐ Because Dünya needed her help with his business.
c ☐ Because she had found out that Dünya was smuggling drugs.
d ☐ Because Dünya didn't want Tom to marry her.

10 Why was Mr Pennington at the villa?
a ☐ Because he had contacted the Turkish police.
b ☐ Because he was working with Mr Dünya.
c ☐ Because he was looking for Tom.
d ☐ Because he lived next door to Mr Dünya.

Unanswered Questions

Answer the questions, using your imagination.

1 Whose body was found in Angela's hired car?

....

....

2 Would Dünya have been caught if he had killed Angela in the
hired car?

....

.ı...

3 Why did Dünya decide to kill Angela after he caught Tom and
Kemal?

....

....

4 How did Dünya smuggle drugs from Turkey to England?

....

....

Published by Macmillan Heinemann ELT
Between Towns Road, Oxford OX4 3PP
Macmillan Heinemann ELT is an imprint of
Macmillan Publishers Limited
Companies and representatives throughout the world
Heinemann is a registered trademark of Pearson Education, used under licence.

ISBN 978-0-2300-3044-2
ISBN 978-1-4050-7705-7 (with CD pack)

Illustrated by Robert Geary
Original cover template design by Jackie Hill
Cover photography by Photodisc Red

Printed in Thailand

2010   2009   2008
6   5   4   3   2

with CD pack

2012   2011   2010
13   12   11   10